ANDREW LLOYD

A Choral
Selection
for Children

A REALLY USEFUL GROUP PUBLICATION
WWW.REALLYUSEFUL.COM

EXCLUSIVE DISTRIBUTORS:
MUSIC SALES LIMITED
14-15 BERNERS STREET, LONDON W1T 3LJ, UK.
MUSIC SALES PTY LIMITED
120 ROTHSCHILD AVENUE, ROSEBERY, NSW 2018, AUSTRALIA.

WWW.MUSICSALES.COM

ORDER NO. RG10527
ISBN 978-1-84772-364-2

EDITED BY RACHEL PAYNE.
ARRANGED BY BARRIE CARSON TURNER.
MUSIC PROCESSED BY PAUL EWERS MUSIC DESIGN.

PRINTED IN THE EU.

ANDREW LLOYD WEBBER

A Choral
Selection
for Children

ANDREW LLOYD WEBBER

A Choral Selection for Children

Any Dream Will Do

from Joseph And The Amazing Technicolor® Dreamcoat

Lyrics by Tim Rice
Music by Andrew Lloyd Webber

cer - tain   what I thought I knew.   Far, far a -

cer - tain   what I thought I knew, what I thought I knew.

-way,   some-one was weep - ing,   But the world was sleep - ing.

Far, far a - way, some-one was weep - ing,   But the world was sleep - ing.

A - ny dream will do. I wore my coat with gold - en

A - ny dream will do. I wore my coat with gold - en

lin - ing, Bright col - ours shin - ing, won-der-ful and

lin - ing, Bright col - ours shin - ing, won-der-ful and

10

new. And in the east the dawn was break - ing,

new. And in the east the dawn was break - ing,

And the world was wak - ing. A - ny dream will do._____ A

And the world was wak - ing. A - ny dream will do._____ A

cresc. *mf*

crash of drums,_ a flash of light,_ My gold - en coat flew out of sight._ The

crash of drums,_ a flash of light,_ My gold - en coat flew out of sight._ The

col-ours fad - ed in - to dark-ness, I was left a - lone._

col-ours fad - ed in - to dark-ness, I was left a - lone, a - lone._

May I re - turn to the be - gin - ning,

May I re - turn to the be - gin - ning,

The light is dim - ming, and the dream is too.

The light is dim - ming, and the dream is too.

The world and I, we still are wait - ing,

The world and I, we still are wait - ing,

rall.

Still he - si - tat - ing. A - ny dream will do.

Still he - si - tat - ing. A - ny dream will do.

Maestoso

Give me my col - oured coat, My a - maz-ing col-oured coat, Give me my

Give me my col - oured coat, My a - maz-ing col-oured coat, Give me my

rall.

col - oured coat, My a - maz - ing col - oured coat._____

col - oured coat, My a - maz - ing___ col - oured_ coat._____

Joseph's Coat

from Joseph And The Amazing Technicolor® Dreamcoat

Lyrics by Tim Rice
Music by Andrew Lloyd Webber

N.B. This song can either be through sung as a full ensemble,
or the parts can be divided up between sections of the chorus.

loved an - oth - er all my life, And Jo - seph was my joy be - cause He re-
Jo - seph was the spe - cial one, So Ja - cob bought his son a coat, A

loved an - oth - er all my life, And Jo - seph was my joy be - cause He re-
Jo - seph was the spe - cial one, So Ja - cob bought his son a coat, A

v. 1 NARRATOR
(v. 2 NARRATOR cont)

-mind - ed me of her.___ Through young Jo - seph,
mul - ti - col - oured coat to wear. Jo - seph's coat was

-mind - ed me of her.___ Through young Jo - seph,
mul - ti - col - oured coat to wear. Jo - seph's coat was

17

Ja - cob lived his youth a - gain.   Loved him, praised him,   gave him all he could but then It
e - le - gant, the coat was fine. The taste - ful   style   was the ul - ti-mate in good de -sign, An

Ja - cob lived his youth a - gain.   Loved him, praised him,   gave him all he could but then It
e - le - gant, the coat was fine. The taste - ful   style   was the ul - ti-mate in good de -sign, An

made   the   rest   feel   se - cond   best,   and   ev - en   if   they
this   is   why   it   caught   the   eye;   a   king   would   stop   and

made   the   rest   feel   se - cond   best,   and   ev - en   if   they
this   is   why   it   caught   the   eye;   a   king   would   stop   and

18

were,____ Be - ing told we're al - so - rans Does not
stare,____ And when Jo - seph tried it on, He knew his

were,____ Be - ing told we're al - so - rans Does not
stare,____ And when Jo - seph tried it on, He knew his

21

make us Jo - seph fans. But where they have real - ly missed the
sheep - skin days were gone, Such a dazz - ling coat of ma - ny

make us Jo - seph fans. But where they have real - ly missed the
sheep - skin days were gone, Such a dazz - ling coat of ma - ny

boat is We're great guys but no - one seems to no - tice. Jo - seph's
col - ours, How he loved his coat of ma - ny col - ours. In a

boat is We're great guys but no - one seems to no - tice. Jo - seph's
col - ours, How he loved his coat of ma - ny col - ours. In a

charm and win - ning smiles Failed to slay them in the
class a - bove the rest, It ev - en went well with his

charm and win - ning smiles Failed to slay them in the
class a - bove the rest, It ev - en went well with his

aisles, And their fa - ther could - n't see the dan - ger, He could
vest, Such a stun - ning coat of ma - ny col - ours, How he

aisles, And their fa - ther could - n't see the dan - ger, He could
vest, Such a stun - ning coat of ma - ny col - ours, How he

not i - ma - gine a - ny dan - ger, He just saw in Jo - seph all his dreams come
loved his coat of ma - ny col - ours, It was red and yel - low and green and brown and

not i - ma - gine a - ny dan - ger, He just saw in Jo - seph all his dreams come
loved his coat of ma - ny col - ours, It was red and yel - low and green and brown and

21

1.

true.

2.

blue.

BROTHERS

mf

We have nev - er

NARRATOR

mf

Jo - seph's bro - thers weren't too pleased with what they saw,

BROTHERS

We have nev - er

mf

liked him all that much be-fore, And now this_ coat_ has got our_ goat,_ We

liked him all that much be-fore, And now this_ coat_ has got our_ goat,_ We

NARRATOR

feel life is un - fair,_ And when Jo - seph graced the scene His bro - thers

NARRATOR

feel life is un - fair, And when Jo - seph graced the scene His bro - thers

23

turned a shade of green, this a-stound-ing cloth-ing took the bis-cuit, Quite the

turned a shade of green, this a-stound-ing cloth-ing took the bis-cuit, Quite the

JOSEPH

smooth-est per-son in the dis-trict, I look hand-some, I look smart, I am a

JOSEPH

smooth-est per-son in the dis-trict, I look hand-some, I look smart, I am a

walk-ing work of art, Such a dazz-ling coat of ma-ny col-ours. How I

walk-ing work of art, Such a dazz-ling coat of ma-ny col-ours. How I

love my coat of ma-ny col-ours. It was red and yel-low and green and brown And

love my coat of ma-ny col-ours. It was red and yel-low and green and brown And

sil - ver and rose And a - zure and le - mon and rus - set and grey And

art, Such a dazz - ling coat of ma - ny col - ours, How I

purple and white and pink and or - ange and red yel - low

love my coat of ma - ny col - ours, It was red and yel - low and

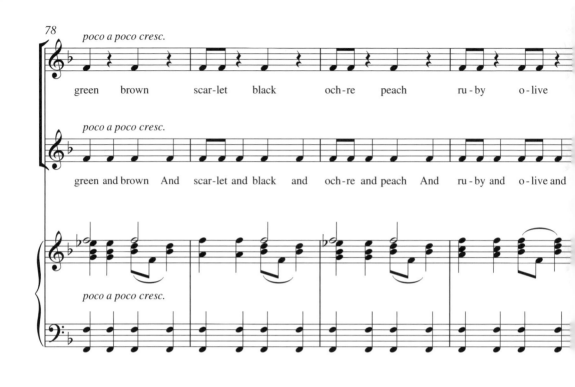

28

cream and crim-son and sil-ver and rose And a-zure and le-mon and

cream and crim-son and sil-ver and rose And a-zure and le-mon and

rus-set and grey And pur-ple and white and pink and or-ange and blue.

rus-set and grey And pur-ple and white and pink and or-ange and blue.

Let Us Love In Peace

from The Beautiful Game

Lyrics by Ben Elton
Music by Andrew Lloyd Webber

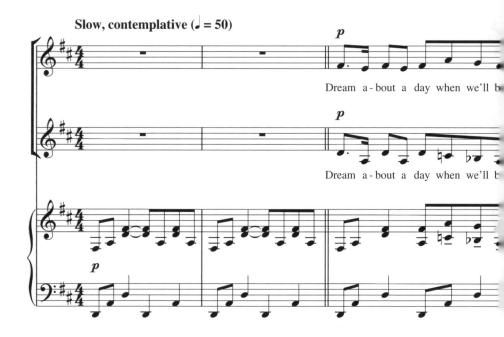

Ask your-self what it would feel like. Dream the dream with all of your might.
Days of hope so calm and tran - quil. Pri - vate mo - ments to be thank - ful.

Ask your-self what it would feel like. Dream the dream with all of your might.
Days of hope so calm and tran - quil. Pri - vate mo - ments to be thank - ful.

Close your eyes, vis - ual - ise, just one nor - mal day.
On our own, left a - lone, free to love in peace.

Close your eyes, vis - ual - ise, just one nor - mal day.
On our own, left a - lone, free to love in peace.

Just i - ma - gine no more vio - lence, no more bombs, the sound of si - lence.

no more vio - lence, the sound of si - lence.

D.S. al Coda
(Verse 2)

Time to be you and me, time to love in peace.

Time to be you and me, time to love in peace.

$\oplus$ **Coda**

Time to dance and time to grow. Time to learn and time to know.

time to grow. and time to know.

rit.

Time to pros - per and in - crease. We'll love in peace.

pros - per and in - crease. We'll love in peace.

cease. Then we'll be free to love in peace.

cease. Then we'll be free to love in peace.

Just for fun, think of one or - di - na - ry day.

Just for fun, think of one or - di - na - ry day.

Macavity: The Mystery Cat

from Cats

Text by T.S. Eliot
Music by Andrew Lloyd Webber

he's the mas - ter cri - mi - nal who can de-fy the law._ He's the baf - fle-ment of Scot-land Yard, the

he's the mas - ter cri - mi - nal who can de-fy the law._ He's the baf - fle-ment of Scot-land Yard, the

Fly - ing Squad's des-pair:_ For when they reach the scene of crime, Mac - a - vi - ty's_ not there.

Fly - ing Squad's des-pair:_ For when they reach the scene of crime, Mac - a - vi - ty's_ not there.

breaks the law of gra - vi - ty. His powers of le - vi - ta - tion_ would make a fa - kir stare,_ An

breaks the law of gra - vi - ty. His powers of le - vi - ta - tion_ would make a fa - kir stare,_ An

when you reach the scene of crime, Mac - a - vi - ty's_ not there! You may seek him in the base - ment, you m

when you reach the scene of crime, Mac - a - vi - ty's_ not there! You may seek him in the base - ment, you m

look up in the air: But I tell you once and once a-gain, Mac-

look up in the air: But I tell you once and once a-gain, Mac-

- a-vi-ty's— not there! Mac - a - vi-ty's a gin-ger cat, he's ve - ry tall and thin;— You would

- a-vi-ty's— not there! Mac - a - vi-ty's a gin-ger cat, he's ve - ry tall and thin;— You would

know him if you saw him, for his eyes are sunk-en in.___ His brow is deep-ly lined with thought, hi

know him if you saw him, for his eyes are sunk-en in.___ His brow is deep-ly lined with thought, hi

head is high-ly domed; His coat is dust-y from ne-glect, his whis - kers are un-combed. H

head is high-ly domed; whis - kers are un-combed.

sways his head from side to side, with move - ments like a snake. And

with move - ments like a snake. And

when you think he's half a- sleep, he's al - ways wide a- wake. Mac -

when you think he's half a- sleep, he's al - ways wide a- wake. Mac -

- a - vi - ty, Mac-a - vi - ty, there's no one like Mac - a - vi - ty, For he's a fiend in fe - line shape, a
- a vi - ty, Mac-a - vi - ty, there's no one like Mac - a - vi - ty, There nev - er was a cat of such de

- a - vi - ty, Mac-a - vi - ty, there's no one like Mac - a - vi - ty, For he's a fiend in fe - line shape, a
- a - vi - ty, Mac-a - vi - ty, there's no one like Mac - a - vi - ty, There nev - er was a cat of such de

mon-ster of de - pra - vi-ty, You may meet him in a by-street, you may see him in the square:_ B
-ceit-ful-ness and sua - vi-ty. He al-ways has an a - li - bi, and one or two to spare:_ WI

mon-ster of de - pra - vi-ty, You may meet him in a by-street, you may see him in the square:_ B
-ceit-ful-ness and sua - vi-ty. He al-ways has an a - li - bi, and one or two to spare:_ WI

when a crime's dis-co-vered, then Mac-a-vi-ty's___ not there! He's
ev - er time the deed took place, Mac-a-vi-ty___ wasn't there! And

when a crime's dis-co-vered, then Mac-a-vi-ty's___ not there! He's
ev - er time the deed took place, Mac-a-vi-ty___ wasn't there! And

out - ward - ly___ re - spect - a - ble.___ (I know_ he cheats_ at
when the Fo - reign Of - fice find_ a trea-ty's gone_ a-

out - ward - ly___ re - spect - a - ble.___ (I know_ he cheats_ at
when the Fo - reign Of - fice find_ a trea-ty's gone_ a-

cards.) And his foot-prints are__ not found__ in a - ny file__ of Scot - lar
stray, Or the Ad - mi - ral - ty lose__ some plans__ or draw-ings by__ th

cards.) And his foot-prints are__ not found__ in a - ny file__ of Scot - lar
stray, Or the Ad - mi - ral - ty lose__ some plans__ or draw-ings by__ th

Yard's And when the lar - der's loot - ed, or the je - wel case is ri - fled,__ o
way, And when the loss has been dis-closed, the Se - cret Ser - vice say: "

Yard's And when the lar - der's loot - ed, or the je - wel case is ri - fled,__ c
way, And when the loss has been dis-closed, the Se - cret Ser - vice say: "

when the milk is miss - ing, or an - oth - er Peke's been sti - fled, Or the
must have been Mac - a - vi - ty!" but he's a mile a - way. You'll be

when the milk is miss - ing, or an - oth - er Peke's been sti - fled, Or the
must have been Mac - a - vi - ty!" but he's a mile a - way. You'll be

1.

green-house glass is bro - ken, and the trel - lis past re - pair,

green-house glass is bro - ken, and the trel - lis past re - pair,

sfz

sfz

There's the won - der of the thing, Mac - a - vi - ty's___ not there! Mac -

There's the won - der of the thing, Mac - a - vi - ty's___ not there! Mac -

sure to find him rest - ing, or a - lick - ing of his thumbs, Or en - gaged in do - ing com - pli - ca - t

sure to find him rest - ing, or a - lick - ing of his thumbs, Or en - gaged in do - ing com - pli - ca - t

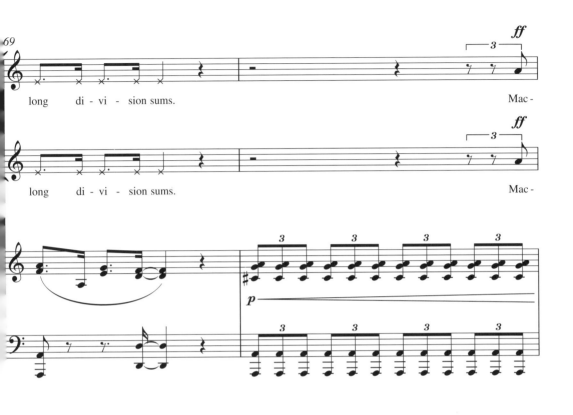

long   di - vi - sion sums.   Mac -

long   di - vi - sion sums.   Mac -

- a - vi - ty, Mac - a - vi - ty, there's no one like Mac - a - vi - ty, There ne - ver was a cat of such de-

- a - vi - ty, Mac - a - vi - ty, there's no one like Mac - a - vi - ty, There ne - ver was a cat of such de-

49

-ceit-ful-ness and sua-vi-ty. He al-way has an a - li- bi, and one or two to spare:_ wha

-ceit-ful-ness and sua-vi-ty. He al-way has an a - li-bi, and one or two to spare:_ wha

-ev - er time the deed took place, Mac - a - vi-ty was-n't there! And they say that all the cats whose wick-e

-ev - er time the deed took place, Mac - a - vi-ty was-n't there! And they say that all the cats whose wick-e

80

deeds are wide - ly known (I might men -tion Mun - go -jer - rie, Rum - pel - tea - zer, Grid - dle- bone)   Are

deeds are wide - ly known (I might men -tion Mun - go -jer - rie, Rum - pel - tea - zer, Grid - dle- bone)   Are

83

no -thing more than a - gents for the cat who all the time_ just con -trols the o - pe -ra- tions: The Na-

no -thing more than a - gents for the cat who all the time_ just con -trols the o - pe -ra- tions: The Na-

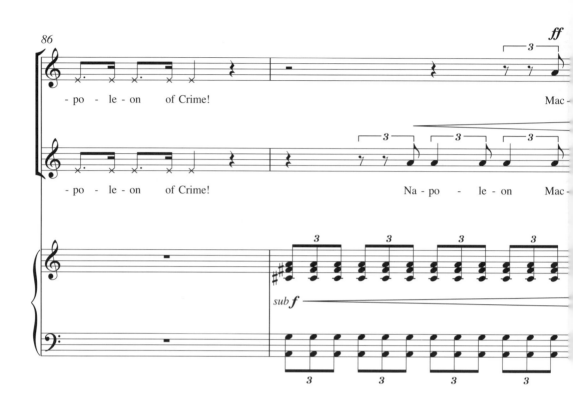

mon - ster of de - pra - vi - ty. You may meet him in a by - street, You may

mon - ster of de - pra - vi - ty. You may meet him in a by - street,

see him in the square:_ But when a crime's dis-co- vered, then Mac - a-vi-ty's not there!

see him in the square:_ But when a crime's dis-co- vered, then Mac - a-vi-ty's not there!

Mr. Mistoffelees

from Cats

Text by T.S. Eliot
Music by Andrew Lloyd Webber

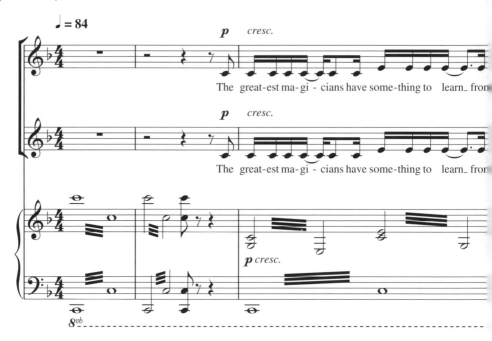

Oh well I nev-er! Was there ev - er a cat so cle-ver as

Oh well I nev-er! Was there ev - er a cat so cle-ver as

Ma - gi - cal Mis - ter Mis- tof - fe - lees! Oh well I nev-er! Was there

Ma - gi - cal Mis - ter Mis- tof - fe - lees! Oh well I nev-er! Was there

ev – er a cat so cle - ver as Ma - gi - cal Mis – ter Mis - tof

ev – er a cat so cle - ver as Ma - gi - cal Mis – ter Mis - tof

- fe - lees!

He is qui - et, he is small, he is black   From hi
His man-ner is vague and a - loof,   You wou

- fe - lees!

he is black   From hi
and a - loof,   You wou

56

19

e - qual-ly cun-ning with dice;   He is   al-ways de-ceiv-ing you in - to be - liev - ing That he
he was a-bout on the roof   (At   least we all heard_ that some-bo-dy purred) Which is

e - qual-ly cun-ning with dice;   That he
he was a-bout on the roof   Which is

21

on - ly hunt - ing for mice.   He can play a - ny trick_ with a   cork   Or a
in - con - test - a - ble proof.   Of his sin-gu-lar ma - gi - cal powers;   And I'v

on - ly hunt - ing for mice.   He can play a - ny trick_ with a   cork   Or a
in - con - test - a - ble proof.   Of his sin-gu-lar ma - gi - cal powers;   And I'v

spoon and a bit of fish paste;   If you look for a knife or a fork   And you
known the fa-mi-ly to call   Him   in from the gar-den for hours   While

spoon and a bit of fish paste;   If you look for a knife or a fork   And you
known the fa-mi-ly to call   Him   in from the gar-den for hours   While

cresc.

think it is mere-ly mis-placed,   You have seen it one mo-ment, and then it is gone! But you'll
he was a-sleep in the hall.   And   not long a-go— this phe-no me-nal cat——— Pro -

cresc.

think it is mere-ly mis-placed,   You have seen it one mo-ment, and then it is gone! But you'll
he was a-sleep in the hall.   And   not long a-go— this phe-no me-nal cat——— Pro -

cresc.

59

find it next week__ ly - ing out on the lawn.__ And we all say:
-duced se - ven kit - tens right out of a hat!__ And we all say:

And we all say:

- fe - less!____

60

Starlight Express

from Starlight Express

Lyrics by Richard Stilgoe
Music by Andrew Lloyd Webber

When your good - nights have been said__ and you are ly - ing in bed__ with the
take me a - way__ but bring me back be - fore day - light, and

When your good - nights have been said__ and you are ly - ing in bed__
take me a - way__ but bring me back be - fore day,__

cov - ers pulled up   tight;___   and though you count ev - ery sheep_ you get the
in   the time_ be - tween___   take me   to   ev - er - y - where_ but don't a

cov - ers pulled up   tight;___   and though you count ev - ery sheep_ you get the
in   the time_ be - tween___   take me   to   ev - er - y - where_ but don't a

feel - ing that sleep_ is going to   stay   a - way_   to - night.___
- ban - don me   there,_   just   want   to   say_   I've been.___   I be

feel - ing that sleep_ is going to   stay   a - way_   to - night.___
- ban - don me   there,_   just   want   to   say_   I've been._

62

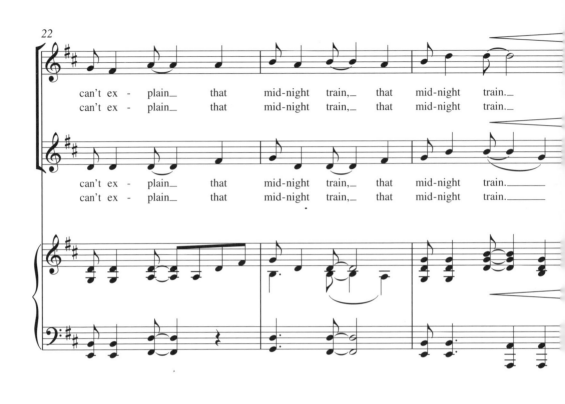

22

can't ex - plain___ that mid-night train,___ that mid-night train.___
can't ex - plain___ that mid-night train,___ that mid-night train.___

can't ex - plain___ that mid-night train,___ that mid-night train.___
can't ex - plain___ that mid-night train,___ that mid-night train.___

25

mf

Star-light Ex - press,___ you must con - fess___ are you real,_____ yes o

mf

Star-light Ex - press,___ are you real,_____ yes o

mf

mf

Star - light,_ Star - light_ Ex - press,

Star-light Ex - press,_ ans-wer me yes,_ I don't want you_ to go._

Star-light Ex - press,_ I don't want you_ to go._

Star-light Ex - press,_ you must con - fess_ are you real,_____ yes or no?

Star-light Ex - press,_ are you real,_____ yes or no?

rit.

Star-light Ex - press,_ ans-wer me yes,_ I don't want you__ to go.

Star-light Ex - press,_ I don't want you__ to go.

No Matter What

from Whistle Down The Wind

Lyrics by Jim Steinman
Music by Andrew Lloyd Webber

teach   us,   What we be - lieve is   true.
ans - wered,   Then we would hear God   say:

No mat - ter what they   teach   us,   What we   be - lieve is___
If   on - ly prayers were ans - wered,   Then we would hear   God__

No mat - ter what they call   us,   How - ev - er they at - tack,
No mat - ter what they tell   you,   No mat - ter what they do,

true.   No mat - ter what they   call   us,   How - ev - er they   at -
say: No mat - ter what they   tell   you,   No mat - ter what they

15

mf

No mat-ter where they take us, We'll find our own way back.___ I
No mat-ter what they teach you, What you be-lieve is true.___ And

mf

-tack, No mat-ter where they take us, We'll find our own way back.___ I
do, No mat-ter what they teach you, What you be-lieve is true.___ And

19

can't de-ny___ what I___ be-lieve,___ I can't be___ what I'm
I will keep_ you safe___ and strong,_ And shel-tered_ from the

can't de-ny___ what I___ be-lieve,___
I will keep_ you safe___ and strong,_

mf

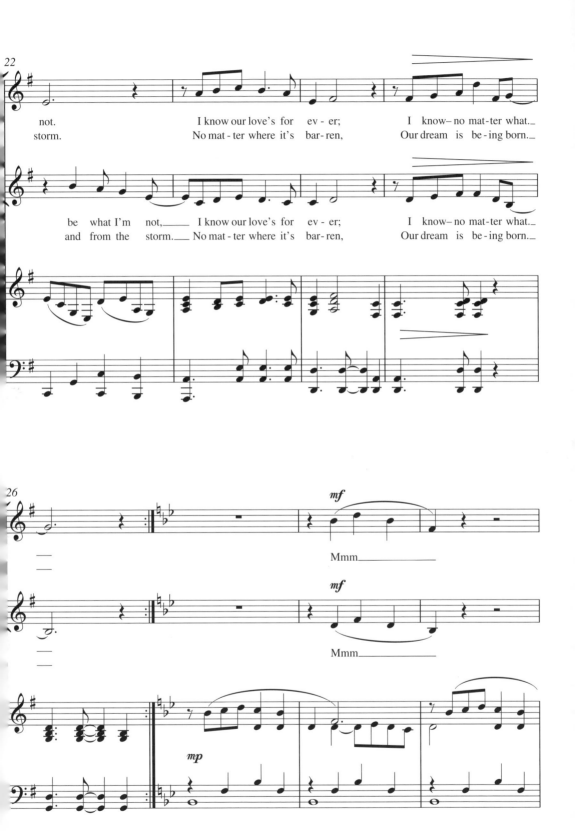

not.
storm.

I know our love's for ev - er;
No mat - ter where it's bar - ren,

I know– no mat-ter what.
Our dream is be-ing born.

be what I'm not,
and from the storm.

I know our love's for ev - er;
No mat - ter where it's bar - ren,

I know– no mat-ter what.
Our dream is be-ing born.

Mmm

Mmm

Mmm_____   Mmm_____

Mmm_____   Mmm_____

No mat-ter who they fol - low,   No mat-ter where they lead,

No mat-ter who they fol - low,   No mat-ter where they

mp

mp

mp

No mat-ter what the end-ing, my life be-gan with you.___ I

No mat-ter what the end-ing, my life be-gan with you.___ I

can't de-ny___ what I___ be-lieve,___ I can't be___ what I'm not.

can't de-ny___ what I___ be-lieve,___

When Children Rule The World

from Whistle Down The Wind

Lyrics by Jim Steinman
Music by Andrew Lloyd Webber

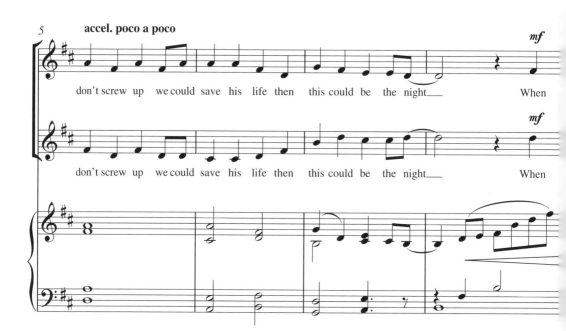

child - ren___ rule the world.___ This could_ be the night,_

child - ren rule the world.___ This could_ be the night,_

___ the night, when child - ren___ rule the world.___

when child - ren___ rule the world.___

Doves and kings and shep-herds and wise - men came to - ge - ther,

Doves and kings and shep-herds and wise - men came to - ge - ther,

fol-lowed the star.__ They all ga - thered down in the man - ger, the

fol-lowed the star.__ They all ga - thered down in the man - ger, the

came from so ve-ry far.___ Mid-night is clear,___ our sa-viour is here,_

came from so ve-ry far.___ Mid-night is clear,_

He's gon-na guard___ each boy and girl._____ No hun-ger or thirst,_

sa-viour is here,_ guard each boy and girl._____

the last will be first,___ the night that child-ren rule the world,___ When

hun-ger or thirst,_ last will be first,_ child-ren rule the world,_ When

child-ren rule the world_ to - night, When child-ren rule the world._

child-ren rule the world_ When child-ren rule the world._

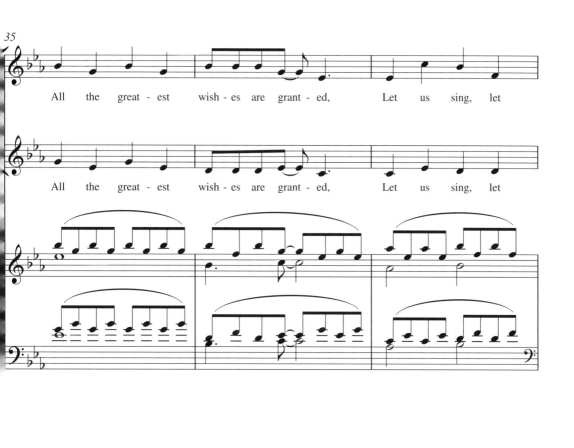

All the great - est wish - es are grant - ed, Let us sing, let

All the great - est wish - es are grant - ed, Let us sing, let

in - no-cence reign._ All the prayers are fi - nal - ly ans - wered,

in - no-cence reign._ All the prayers are fi - nal - ly ans - wered,

Lyrics

JOSEPH'S COAT

Lyrics by Tim Rice Music by Andrew Lloyd Webber

Jacob: Joseph's mother,
She was quite my favourite wife,
I never really loved another all my life,
And Joseph was my joy because
He reminded me of her.

Narrator: Through young Joseph,
Jacob lived his youth again.
Loved him, praised him,
Gave him all he could but then
It made the rest feel second best,

Brothers: And even if they were,
Being told we're also-rans
Does not makes us Joseph fans.
But where they have really missed the boat is
We're great guys but no-one seems to notice.

Narrator: Joseph's charm and winning smiles
Failed to slay them in the aisle,
And their father couldn't see the danger,
He could not imagine any danger,
He just saw in Joseph all his dreams come true.

Jacob wanted to show the world
He loved his son,
To make it clear that
Joseph was the special one,
So Jacob bought his son a coat,
A multi-coloured coat to wear.

Joseph's coat was elegant, the cut was fine.
The tasteful style was the ultimate in good design,
And this is why it caught the eye;
A king would stop and stare,

And when Joseph tried it on,
He knew his sheepskin days were gone,
Such a dazzling coat of many colours,
How he loved his coat of many colours

In a class above the rest,
It even went well with his vest,
Such a stunning coat of many colours,
How he loved his coat of many colours,
It was red and yellow and green and brown and blue.

Joseph's brothers
Weren't too pleased with what they saw,

Brothers: We have never liked him all that much before,
And now this coat has got our goat,
We feel life is unfair,

Narrator: And when Joseph graced the scene
His brothers turned a shade of green,
This astounding clothing took the biscuit,
Quite the smoothest person in the district,

Joseph: I look handsome, I look smart,
I am walking work of art,
Such a dazzling coat of colours.
How I love my coat of many colours.

All: It was red and yellow and green and brown
And scarlet and black and ochre and peach
And ruby and olive and violet and fawn
And lilac and gold and chocolate and mauve
And cream and crimson and silver and rose
And azure and lemon and russet and grey
And purple and white and pink and orange
And red and yellow and green and brown
And scarlet and black and ochre and peach
And ruby and olive and violet and fawn
And lilac and gold and chocolate and mauve
And cream and crimson and silver and rose
And azure and lemon and russet and grey
And purple and white and pink and orange and blue.

ANY DREAM WILL DO

Lyrics by Tim Rice Music by Andrew Lloyd Webber

I closed my eyes,
Drew back the curtain,
To see for certain
What I thought I knew.
Far, far away,
Someone was weeping,
But the world was sleeping.
Any dream will do.

I wore my coat
With golden lining,
Bright colours shining,
Wonderful and new.
And in the east,
The dawn was breaking,
And the world was waking.
Any dream will do.

A crash of drums, a flash of light,
My golden coat flew out of sight.
The colours faded into darkness,
I was left alone.

May I return
To the beginning,
The light is dimming,
And the dream is too.
The world and I,
We are still waiting,
Still hesitating.
Any dream will do.

Give me my coloured coat,
my amazing coloured coat,
Give me my coloured coat,
my amazing coloured coat.

Let Us Love In Peace

Lyrics by Ben Elton Music by Andrew Lloyd Webber

Close your eyes, visualise,
Just one normal day.

Time to find out who we are.
Time to find our lucky star.
Time for all our pains to cease.
We'll love in peace.

Just imagine no more violence,
No more bombs, the sound of
silence.
Time to be you and me,
Time to love in peace.

Dream about a day when we'll be
Calm, serene, completely carefree.
Just for fun, think of one
Ordinary day.

Days of hope so calm and tranquil.
Private moments to be thankful.
On our own, left alone,
Free to love in peace.

Time to simply sit and breathe.
Time to learn how to believe.
And give thanks for our release,
To love in peace.

Just imagine no more violence,
No more bombs, the sound of silence.
Time to be you and me,
Time to love in peace.

Time to dance and time to grow.
Time to learn and time to know.
Time to prosper and increase.
We'll love in peace.

Sometimes I get on my knees and pray
For that one ordinary day
When all the pain will finally cease.
Then we'll be free to love in peace.

Just for fun, think of one
Ordinary day.

MACAVITY: THE MYSTERY CAT

Text by T.S. Eliot Music by Andrew Lloyd Webber

Macavity's a mystery cat:
he's called the Hidden Paw,
For he's the master criminal
who can defy the law.
He's the bafflement of Scotland Yard,
the Flying Squad's despair:
For when they reach the scene of crime,
Macavity's not there.

Macavity, Macavity,
there's no one like Macavity,
He's broken every human law,
he breaks the law of gravity.
His powers of levitation
would make a fakir stare,
And when you reach the scene of crime
Macavity's not there!
You may seek him in the basement,
you may look up in the air:
But I tell you once and once again,
Macavity's not there!

Macavity's a ginger cat,
he's very tall and thin;
You would know him if you saw him,
for his eyes are sunken in.
His brow is deeply lined in thought,
his head is highly domed;
His coat is dusty from neglect,
his whiskers are uncombed.
He sways his head from side to side,
with movements like a snake.
And when you think he's half asleep,
he's always wide awake.

Macavity, Macavity,
there's no one like Macavity,
For he's a fiend in feline shape,
a monster of depravity,
You may meet him in a by-street,
you may see him in the square:
But when a crime's discovered,
then Macavity's not there!

He's outwardly respectable.
(I know he cheats at cards.)
And his footprints are not found
any file of Scotland Yard's
And when the larder's looted,
or the jewel case is rifled,
Or when the milk is missing,
or another Peke's been stifled,
Or the greenhouse glass is broke
and the trellis past repair,
There's the wonder of the thing,
Macavity's not there!

Macavity, Macavity,
there's no one like Macavity,
There never was a cat of such
deceitfulness and suavity.
He always has an alibi,
and one or two to spare:
Whatever time the deed took pla
Macavity wasn't there!

And when the Foreign Office find
a treaty's gone astray,
Or the Admiralty lose some plans
or drawings by the way,
And when the loss has been disclosed,
the Secret Service say:
"It must have been Macavity!"
but he's a mile away.
You'll be sure to find him resting,
or a-licking of his thumbs,
Or engaged in doing complicated
long division sums.

Macavity, Macavity,
there's no one like Macavity,
There never was a cat of such
deceitfulness and suavity.
He always has an alibi,
and one or two to spare:
Whatever time the deed took place,
Macavity wasn't there!

And they say that all the cats whose
wicked deeds are widely known
(I might mention Mungojerrie,
Rumpelteazer, Griddlebone)
Are nothing more than agents
for the cat who all the time
Just controls the operations:
The Napoleon of Crime!

Macavity, Macavity,
there's no one like Macavity,
He's a fiend in feline shape,
a monster of depravity.
You may meet him in a by-street,
you may see him in the square:
But when a crime's discovered,
then Macavity's not there!

MR. MISTOFFELEES

Text by T.S. Eliot   Music by Andrew Lloyd Webber

The greatest magicians have something to learn
From Mister Mistoffelees's Conjuring Turn.
Presto! And we all say:

Oh well I never! Was there ever
A cat so clever as Magical Mister Mistoffelees!
Oh well I never! Was there ever
A cat so clever as Magical Mister Mistoffelees!

He is quiet, he is small, he is black
From the ears to the tip of his tail:
He can creep through the tiniest crack,
He can walk on the narrowest rail.

He can pick any card from a pack,
He is equally cunning with dice;
He is always deceiving you into believing
That he's only hunting for mice.

He can play any trick with a cork
Or a spoon and a bit of fish paste;
If you look for a knife or a fork
And you think it was merely misplaced,

You have seen it one moment,
and then it is gone!
But you find it next week
lying out on the lawn.
And we all say:

Oh well I never! Was there ever
A cat so clever as Magical Mister Mistoffelees!
Oh well I never! Was there ever
A cat so clever as Magical Mister Mistoffelees!

His manner is vague and aloof,
You would think there was nobody shyer,
But his voice has been heard on the roof
When he was curled up by the fire.

And he's sometimes been heard by the fire,
When he was about on the roof
(At least we all heard that somebody purred)
Which is incontestable proof.
Of his singular magical powers;
And I've known the family to call
Him in from the garden for hours
When he was asleep in the hall.

And not long ago this phenomenal cat
Produced seven kittens right out of a hat!
And we all say:

Oh well I never! Was there ever
A cat so clever as Magical Mister Mistoffelees!
Oh well I never! Was there ever
A cat so clever as Magical Mister Mistoffelees!

STARLIGHT EXPRESS

Lyrics by Richard Stilgoe Music by Andrew Lloyd Webber

When your goodnights have been said
And you are lying in bed
With the covers pulled up tight;
And though you count every sheep
You get the feeling that sleep
Is going to stay away tonight.

That's when you hear it coming,
That's when you hear the humming
Of the midnight train, Here again;
Can't explain that midnight train,
That midnight train.

Starlight Express, you must confess
Are you real, yes or no?
Starlight Express, answer me yes
I don't want you to go.

Want you to take me away
But bring me back before daylight,
And in the time between
Take me to everywhere
But don't abandom me there,
Just want to say I've been.

I believe in you completely
Though I may be dreaming sweetly,
I can hear the train, Here again;
Can't explain that midnight train,
That midnight train.

Starlight Express, you must confess
Are you real, yes or no?
Starlight Express, answer me yes
I don't want you to go.

Starlight, Starlight Express,
Starlight Express, answer me yes,
I don't want you to go.
Starlight Express, you must confess
Are you real, yes or no!
Starlight Express, answer me yes,
I don't want you to go.

No Matter What

Lyrics by Jim Steinman   Music by Andrew Lloyd Webber

No matter what they tell us,
No matter what they do,
No matter what they teach us,
What we believe is true.

No matter what they call us,
However they attack,
No matter where they take us,
We'll find our own way back.

I can't deny what I believe,
I can't be what I'm not.
I know our love's forever;
I know- no matter what.

If only tears were laughter,
If only night was day,
If only prayers were answered,
Then we would hear God say:

No matter what they tell you,
No matter what they do,
No matter what they teach you,
What you believe is true.

And I will keep you safe and strong,
And sheltered from the storm.
No matter where it's barren,
Our dream is being born.

No matter who they follow,
No matter where they lead,
No matter how they judge us,
I'll be everyone you need.

No matter if the sun don't shine
Or if the skies are blue;
No matter what the ending,
My life began with you.

I can't deny what I believe,
I can't be what I'm not.
I know this love's forever:
I know no matter what.

WHEN CHILDREN RULE THE WORLD

Lyrics by Jim Steinman Music by Andrew Lloyd Webber

We've gotta keep this secret, we gotta do this right.
If we don't screw up we could save his life
Then this could be the night
When children rule the world.
This could be the night, the night,
When children rule the world.

Doves and kings and shepherds and wisemen
Came together, followed the star.
They all gathered down in a manger,
They came from so very far.

Midnight is clear, our saviour is here,
He's gonna guard each boy and girl.
No hunger or thirst, the last will be first,
The night that children rule the world,
When children rule the world tonight,
When children rule the world.

All our greatest wishes are granted,
Let us sing, let innocence reign.
All the prayers are finally answered,
Blessed and free of all pain.

Towers of fire, rise ever higher,
Magical flags will be unfurled.
The demons are gone, The young are the strong
The night that children rule the world,
When children rule the world tonight,
When children rule the world.

Towers of fire, rise ever higher,
Magical flags will be unfurled.
The demons are gone, the young are the strong
The night that children rule the world,
When children rule the world tonight,
When children rule the world.

When children rule the world tonight,
When children rule the world!

1 2 3 4 5 6 7